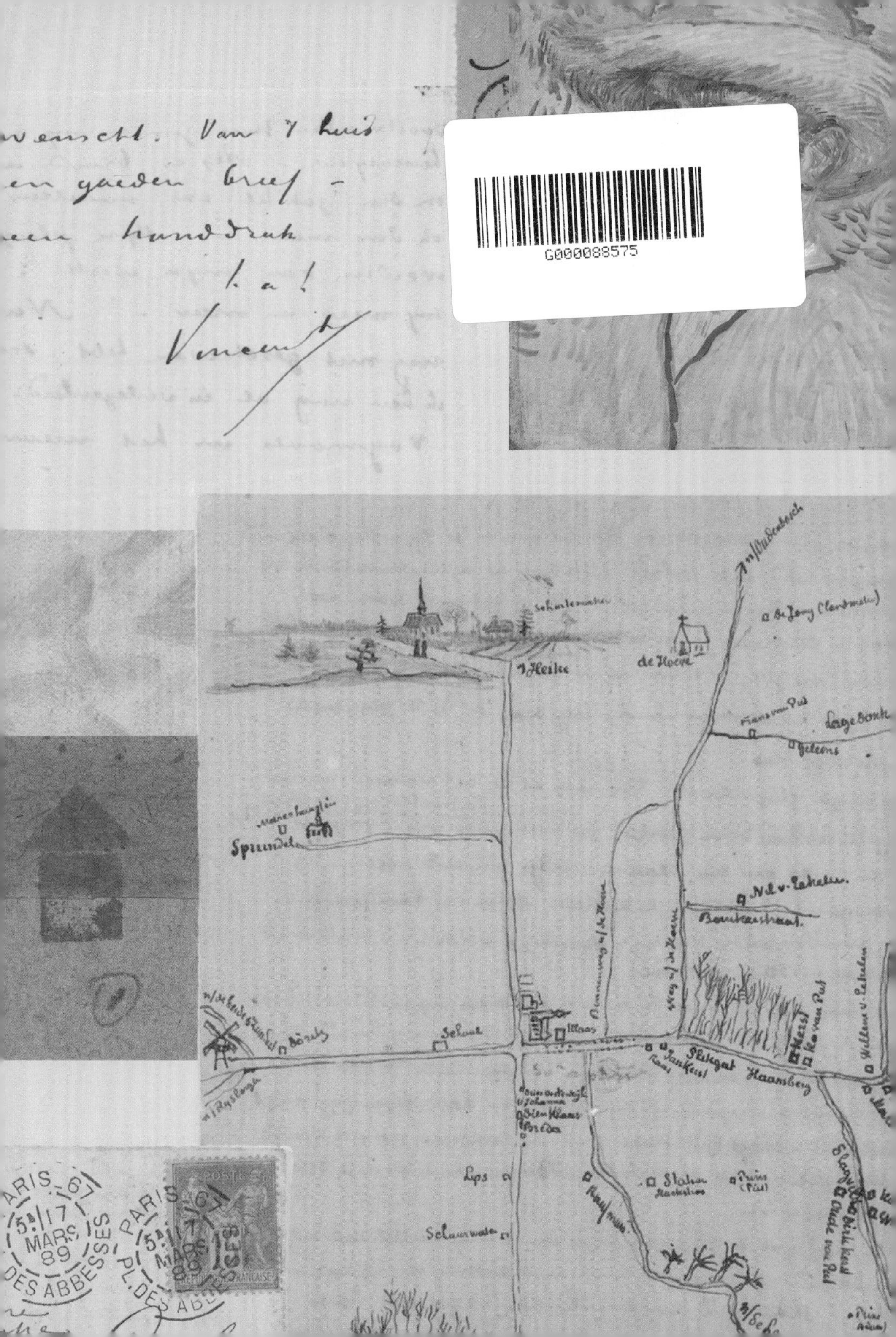

wenscht. Van 't huis
en goeden brief -
een handdruk
t. a.!
Vincent
de Hoeve
PARIS 67
MARS 89
PL. DES ABBESSES
POSTES

Van Gogh
Museum

Amsterdam

Your purchase supports the work of
the Van Gogh Museum

© Van Gogh Museum®

vangoghmuseum.com

Published by Danilo Promotions Ltd. Unit 3, The io Centre, Lea Road, Waltham Abbey, EN9 1AS, England.
Enquiries: info@danilo.com  For all other information: www.danilo.com
Manufactured in China.

# PERSONAL INFORMATION

NAME:

ADDRESS:

MOBILE:

EMAIL:

# IN CASE OF EMERGENCY PLEASE CONTACT

NAME:

ADDRESS:

MOBILE:

DOCTOR:

DOCTOR TELEPHONE:

KNOWN ALLERGIES:

'Enjoy yourself too much, rather than too little, and don't take art or love too seriously either'

**Vincent van Gogh to his sister, Willemien, October 1887**

## JANUARY

| WK | M | T | W | T | F | S | S |
|----|----|----|----|----|----|----|----|
| 52 |    |    |    |    |    |    | 1 |
| 1  | 2  | 3  | 4  | 5  | 6  | 7  | 8 |
| 2  | 9  | 10 | 11 | 12 | 13 | 14 | 15 |
| 3  | 16 | 17 | 18 | 19 | 20 | 21 | 22 |
| 4  | 23 | 24 | 25 | 26 | 27 | 28 | 29 |
| 5  | 30 | 31 |    |    |    |    |   |

## FEBRUARY

| WK | M | T | W | T | F | S | S |
|----|----|----|----|----|----|----|----|
| 5  |    |    | 1  | 2  | 3  | 4  | 5 |
| 6  | 6  | 7  | 8  | 9  | 10 | 11 | 12 |
| 7  | 13 | 14 | 15 | 16 | 17 | 18 | 19 |
| 8  | 20 | 21 | 22 | 23 | 24 | 25 | 26 |
| 9  | 27 | 28 |    |    |    |    |   |

## MARCH

| WK | M | T | W | T | F | S | S |
|----|----|----|----|----|----|----|----|
| 9  |    |    | 1  | 2  | 3  | 4  | 5 |
| 10 | 6  | 7  | 8  | 9  | 10 | 11 | 12 |
| 11 | 13 | 14 | 15 | 16 | 17 | 18 | 19 |
| 12 | 20 | 21 | 22 | 23 | 24 | 25 | 26 |
| 13 | 27 | 28 | 29 | 30 | 31 |    |   |

## APRIL

| WK | M | T | W | T | F | S | S |
|----|----|----|----|----|----|----|----|
| 13 |    |    |    |    |    | 1  | 2 |
| 14 | 3  | 4  | 5  | 6  | 7  | 8  | 9 |
| 15 | 10 | 11 | 12 | 13 | 14 | 15 | 16 |
| 16 | 17 | 18 | 19 | 20 | 21 | 22 | 23 |
| 17 | 24 | 25 | 26 | 27 | 28 | 29 | 30 |

## MAY

| WK | M | T | W | T | F | S | S |
|----|----|----|----|----|----|----|----|
| 18 | 1  | 2  | 3  | 4  | 5  | 6  | 7 |
| 19 | 8  | 9  | 10 | 11 | 12 | 13 | 14 |
| 20 | 15 | 16 | 17 | 18 | 19 | 20 | 21 |
| 21 | 22 | 23 | 24 | 25 | 26 | 27 | 28 |
| 22 | 29 | 30 | 31 |    |    |    |   |

## JUNE

| WK | M | T | W | T | F | S | S |
|----|----|----|----|----|----|----|----|
| 22 |    |    |    | 1  | 2  | 3  | 4 |
| 23 | 5  | 6  | 7  | 8  | 9  | 10 | 11 |
| 24 | 12 | 13 | 14 | 15 | 16 | 17 | 18 |
| 25 | 19 | 20 | 21 | 22 | 23 | 24 | 25 |
| 26 | 26 | 27 | 28 | 29 | 30 |    |   |

## JULY

| WK | M | T | W | T | F | S | S |
|----|----|----|----|----|----|----|----|
| 26 |    |    |    |    |    | 1  | 2 |
| 27 | 3  | 4  | 5  | 6  | 7  | 8  | 9 |
| 28 | 10 | 11 | 12 | 13 | 14 | 15 | 16 |
| 29 | 17 | 18 | 19 | 20 | 21 | 22 | 23 |
| 30 | 24 | 25 | 26 | 27 | 28 | 29 | 30 |
| 31 | 31 |    |    |    |    |    |   |

## AUGUST

| WK | M | T | W | T | F | S | S |
|----|----|----|----|----|----|----|----|
| 31 |    | 1  | 2  | 3  | 4  | 5  | 6 |
| 32 | 7  | 8  | 9  | 10 | 11 | 12 | 13 |
| 33 | 14 | 15 | 16 | 17 | 18 | 19 | 20 |
| 34 | 21 | 22 | 23 | 24 | 25 | 26 | 27 |
| 35 | 28 | 29 | 30 | 31 |    |    |   |

## SEPTEMBER

| WK | M | T | W | T | F | S | S |
|----|----|----|----|----|----|----|----|
| 35 |    |    |    |    | 1  | 2  | 3 |
| 36 | 4  | 5  | 6  | 7  | 8  | 9  | 10 |
| 37 | 11 | 12 | 13 | 14 | 15 | 16 | 17 |
| 38 | 18 | 19 | 20 | 21 | 22 | 23 | 24 |
| 39 | 25 | 26 | 27 | 28 | 29 | 30 |   |

## OCTOBER

| WK | M | T | W | T | F | S | S |
|----|----|----|----|----|----|----|----|
| 39 |    |    |    |    |    |    | 1 |
| 40 | 2  | 3  | 4  | 5  | 6  | 7  | 8 |
| 41 | 9  | 10 | 11 | 12 | 13 | 14 | 15 |
| 42 | 16 | 17 | 18 | 19 | 20 | 21 | 22 |
| 43 | 23 | 24 | 25 | 26 | 27 | 28 | 29 |
| 44 | 30 | 31 |    |    |    |    |   |

## NOVEMBER

| WK | M | T | W | T | F | S | S |
|----|----|----|----|----|----|----|----|
| 44 |    |    | 1  | 2  | 3  | 4  | 5 |
| 45 | 6  | 7  | 8  | 9  | 10 | 11 | 12 |
| 46 | 13 | 14 | 15 | 16 | 17 | 18 | 19 |
| 47 | 20 | 21 | 22 | 23 | 24 | 25 | 26 |
| 48 | 27 | 28 | 29 | 30 |    |    |   |

## DECEMBER

| WK | M | T | W | T | F | S | S |
|----|----|----|----|----|----|----|----|
| 48 |    |    |    |    | 1  | 2  | 3 |
| 49 | 4  | 5  | 6  | 7  | 8  | 9  | 10 |
| 50 | 11 | 12 | 13 | 14 | 15 | 16 | 17 |
| 51 | 18 | 19 | 20 | 21 | 22 | 23 | 24 |
| 52 | 25 | 26 | 27 | 28 | 29 | 30 | 31 |

# 2024 YEAR TO VIEW

## JANUARY

| WK | M | T | W | T | F | S | S |
|----|----|----|----|----|----|----|----|
| 1 | 1 | 2 | 3 | 4 | 5 | 6 | 7 |
| 2 | 8 | 9 | 10 | 11 | 12 | 13 | 14 |
| 3 | 15 | 16 | 17 | 18 | 19 | 20 | 21 |
| 4 | 22 | 23 | 24 | 25 | 26 | 27 | 28 |
| 5 | 29 | 30 | 31 | | | | |

## FEBRUARY

| WK | M | T | W | T | F | S | S |
|----|----|----|----|----|----|----|----|
| 5 | | | | 1 | 2 | 3 | 4 |
| 6 | 5 | 6 | 7 | 8 | 9 | 10 | 11 |
| 7 | 12 | 13 | 14 | 15 | 16 | 17 | 18 |
| 8 | 19 | 20 | 21 | 22 | 23 | 24 | 25 |
| 9 | 26 | 27 | 28 | 29 | | | |

## MARCH

| WK | M | T | W | T | F | S | S |
|----|----|----|----|----|----|----|----|
| 9 | | | | | 1 | 2 | 3 |
| 10 | 4 | 5 | 6 | 7 | 8 | 9 | 10 |
| 11 | 11 | 12 | 13 | 14 | 15 | 16 | 17 |
| 12 | 18 | 19 | 20 | 21 | 22 | 23 | 24 |
| 13 | 25 | 26 | 27 | 28 | 29 | 30 | 31 |

## APRIL

| WK | M | T | W | T | F | S | S |
|----|----|----|----|----|----|----|----|
| 14 | 1 | 2 | 3 | 4 | 5 | 6 | 7 |
| 15 | 8 | 9 | 10 | 11 | 12 | 13 | 14 |
| 16 | 15 | 16 | 17 | 18 | 19 | 20 | 21 |
| 17 | 22 | 23 | 24 | 25 | 26 | 27 | 28 |
| 18 | 29 | 30 | | | | | |

## MAY

| WK | M | T | W | T | F | S | S |
|----|----|----|----|----|----|----|----|
| 18 | | 1 | 2 | 3 | 4 | 5 |
| 19 | 6 | 7 | 8 | 9 | 10 | 11 | 12 |
| 20 | 13 | 14 | 15 | 16 | 17 | 18 | 19 |
| 21 | 20 | 21 | 22 | 23 | 24 | 25 | 26 |
| 22 | 27 | 28 | 29 | 30 | 31 | | |

## JUNE

| WK | M | T | W | T | F | S | S |
|----|----|----|----|----|----|----|----|
| 22 | | | | | | 1 | 2 |
| 23 | 3 | 4 | 5 | 6 | 7 | 8 | 9 |
| 24 | 10 | 11 | 12 | 13 | 14 | 15 | 16 |
| 25 | 17 | 18 | 19 | 20 | 21 | 22 | 23 |
| 26 | 24 | 25 | 26 | 27 | 28 | 29 | 30 |

## JULY

| WK | M | T | W | T | F | S | S |
|----|----|----|----|----|----|----|----|
| 27 | 1 | 2 | 3 | 4 | 5 | 6 | 7 |
| 28 | 8 | 9 | 10 | 11 | 12 | 13 | 14 |
| 29 | 15 | 16 | 17 | 18 | 19 | 20 | 21 |
| 30 | 22 | 23 | 24 | 25 | 26 | 27 | 28 |
| 31 | 29 | 30 | 31 | | | | |

## AUGUST

| WK | M | T | W | T | F | S | S |
|----|----|----|----|----|----|----|----|
| 31 | | | | 1 | 2 | 3 | 4 |
| 32 | 5 | 6 | 7 | 8 | 9 | 10 | 11 |
| 33 | 12 | 13 | 14 | 15 | 16 | 17 | 18 |
| 34 | 19 | 20 | 21 | 22 | 23 | 24 | 25 |
| 35 | 26 | 27 | 28 | 29 | 30 | 31 | |

## SEPTEMBER

| WK | M | T | W | T | F | S | S |
|----|----|----|----|----|----|----|----|
| 35 | | | | | | | 1 |
| 36 | 2 | 3 | 4 | 5 | 6 | 7 | 8 |
| 37 | 9 | 10 | 11 | 12 | 13 | 14 | 15 |
| 38 | 16 | 17 | 18 | 19 | 20 | 21 | 22 |
| 39 | 23 | 24 | 25 | 26 | 27 | 28 | 29 |
| 40 | 30 | | | | | | |

## OCTOBER

| WK | M | T | W | T | F | S | S |
|----|----|----|----|----|----|----|----|
| 40 | | 1 | 2 | 3 | 4 | 5 | 6 |
| 41 | 7 | 8 | 9 | 10 | 11 | 12 | 13 |
| 42 | 14 | 15 | 16 | 17 | 18 | 19 | 20 |
| 43 | 21 | 22 | 23 | 24 | 25 | 26 | 27 |
| 44 | 28 | 29 | 30 | 31 | | | |

## NOVEMBER

| WK | M | T | W | T | F | S | S |
|----|----|----|----|----|----|----|----|
| 44 | | | | 1 | 2 | 3 |
| 45 | 4 | 5 | 6 | 7 | 8 | 9 | 10 |
| 46 | 11 | 12 | 13 | 14 | 15 | 16 | 17 |
| 47 | 18 | 19 | 20 | 21 | 22 | 23 | 24 |
| 48 | 25 | 26 | 27 | 28 | 29 | 30 | |

## DECEMBER

| WK | M | T | W | T | F | S | S |
|----|----|----|----|----|----|----|----|
| 48 | | | | | | | 1 |
| 49 | 2 | 3 | 4 | 5 | 6 | 7 | 8 |
| 50 | 9 | 10 | 11 | 12 | 13 | 14 | 15 |
| 51 | 16 | 17 | 18 | 19 | 20 | 21 | 22 |
| 52 | 23 | 24 | 25 | 26 | 27 | 28 | 29 |
| 1 | 30 | 31 | | | | | |

# NOTABLE DATES

## 2023

| | |
|---|---|
| New Year's Day | JAN 1 |
| New Year Holiday | JAN 2 |
| Bank Holiday (Scotland) | JAN 3 |
| Chinese New Year (Rabbit) | JAN 22 |
| Valentine's Day | FEB 14 |
| Shrove Tuesday | FEB 21 |
| St. David's Day | MAR 1 |
| St. Patrick's Day | MAR 17 |
| Mothering Sunday (UK) | MAR 19 |
| Ramadan Begins | MAR 22 |
| Daylight Saving Time Starts | MAR 26 |
| Passover Begins | APR 5 |
| Good Friday | APR 7 |
| Easter Sunday | APR 9 |
| Easter Monday | APR 10 |
| Earth Day | APR 22 |
| St. George's Day | APR 23 |
| Early May Bank Holiday | MAY 1 |
| Spring Bank Holiday | MAY 29 |
| Father's Day (UK) | JUN 18 |
| Public Holiday (Northern Ireland) | JUL 12 |
| Islamic New Year Begins | JUL 18 |
| Summer Bank Holiday (Scotland) | AUG 7 |
| Summer Bank Holiday (ENG, NIR, WAL) | AUG 28 |
| Rosh Hashanah (Jewish New Year) Begins | SEPT 15 |
| International Day of Peace (United Nations) | SEPT 21 |
| Yom Kippur Begins | SEPT 24 |
| World Mental Health Day | OCT 10 |
| Daylight Saving Time Ends | OCT 29 |
| Halloween | OCT 31 |
| Guy Fawkes Night | NOV 5 |
| Diwali / Remembrance Sunday | NOV 12 |
| St. Andrew's Day | NOV 30 |
| Christmas Day | DEC 25 |
| Boxing Day | DEC 26 |
| New Year's Eve | DEC 31 |

# PLANNER 2023

| JANUARY | FEBRUARY | MARCH |
|---------|----------|-------|
| 1 S | 1 W | 1 W |
| 2 M | 2 T | 2 T |
| 3 T | 3 F | 3 F |
| 4 W | 4 S | 4 S |
| 5 T | 5 S | 5 S |
| 6 F | 6 M | 6 M |
| 7 S | 7 T | 7 T |
| 8 S | 8 W | 8 W |
| 9 M | 9 T | 9 T |
| 10 T | 10 F | 10 F |
| 11 W | 11 S | 11 S |
| 12 T | 12 S | 12 S |
| 13 F | 13 M | 13 M |
| 14 S | 14 T | 14 T |
| 15 S | 15 W | 15 W |
| 16 M | 16 T | 16 T |
| 17 T | 17 F | 17 F |
| 18 W | 18 S | 18 S |
| 19 T | 19 S | 19 S |
| 20 F | 20 M | 20 M |
| 21 S | 21 T | 21 T |
| 22 S | 22 W | 22 W |
| 23 M | 23 T | 23 T |
| 24 T | 24 F | 24 F |
| 25 W | 25 S | 25 S |
| 26 T | 26 S | 26 S |
| 27 F | 27 M | 27 M |
| 28 S | 28 T | 28 T |
| 29 S | | 29 W |
| 30 M | | 30 T |
| 31 T | | 31 F |

| APRIL | MAY | JUNE |
|---|---|---|
| 1 S | 1 M | 1 T |
| 2 S | 2 T | 2 F |
| 3 M | 3 W | 3 S |
| 4 T | 4 T | 4 S |
| 5 W | 5 F | 5 M |
| 6 T | 6 S | 6 T |
| 7 F | 7 S | 7 W |
| 8 S | 8 M | 8 T |
| 9 S | 9 T | 9 F |
| 10 M | 10 W | 10 S |
| 11 T | 11 T | 11 S |
| 12 W | 12 F | 12 M |
| 13 T | 13 S | 13 T |
| 14 F | 14 S | 14 W |
| 15 S | 15 M | 15 T |
| 16 S | 16 T | 16 F |
| 17 M | 17 W | 17 S |
| 18 T | 18 T | 18 S |
| 19 W | 19 F | 19 M |
| 20 T | 20 S | 20 T |
| 21 F | 21 S | 21 W |
| 22 S | 22 M | 22 T |
| 23 S | 23 T | 23 F |
| 24 M | 24 W | 24 S |
| 25 T | 25 T | 25 S |
| 26 W | 26 F | 26 M |
| 27 T | 27 S | 27 T |
| 28 F | 28 S | 28 W |
| 29 S | 29 M | 29 T |
| 30 S | 30 T | 30 F |
|  | 31 W |  |

# PLANNER 2023

| JULY | AUGUST | SEPTEMBER |
|------|--------|-----------|
| 1 S | 1 T | 1 F |
| 2 S | 2 W | 2 S |
| 3 M | 3 T | 3 S |
| 4 T | 4 F | 4 M |
| 5 W | 5 S | 5 T |
| 6 T | 6 S | 6 W |
| 7 F | 7 M | 7 T |
| 8 S | 8 T | 8 F |
| 9 S | 9 W | 9 S |
| 10 M | 10 T | 10 S |
| 11 T | 11 F | 11 M |
| 12 W | 12 S | 12 T |
| 13 T | 13 S | 13 W |
| 14 F | 14 M | 14 T |
| 15 S | 15 T | 15 F |
| 16 S | 16 W | 16 S |
| 17 M | 17 T | 17 S |
| 18 T | 18 F | 18 M |
| 19 W | 19 S | 19 T |
| 20 T | 20 S | 20 W |
| 21 F | 21 M | 21 T |
| 22 S | 22 T | 22 F |
| 23 S | 23 W | 23 S |
| 24 M | 24 T | 24 S |
| 25 T | 25 F | 25 M |
| 26 W | 26 S | 26 T |
| 27 T | 27 S | 27 W |
| 28 F | 28 M | 28 T |
| 29 S | 29 T | 29 F |
| 30 S | 30 W | 30 S |
| 31 M | 31 T | |

| OCTOBER | NOVEMBER | DECEMBER |
|---|---|---|
| 1 S | 1 W | 1 F |
| 2 M | 2 T | 2 S |
| 3 T | 3 F | 3 S |
| 4 W | 4 S | 4 M |
| 5 T | 5 S | 5 T |
| 6 F | 6 M | 6 W |
| 7 S | 7 T | 7 T |
| 8 S | 8 W | 8 F |
| 9 M | 9 T | 9 S |
| 10 T | 10 F | 10 S |
| 11 W | 11 S | 11 M |
| 12 T | 12 S | 12 T |
| 13 F | 13 M | 13 W |
| 14 S | 14 T | 14 T |
| 15 S | 15 W | 15 F |
| 16 M | 16 T | 16 S |
| 17 T | 17 F | 17 S |
| 18 W | 18 S | 18 M |
| 19 T | 19 S | 19 T |
| 20 F | 20 M | 20 W |
| 21 S | 21 T | 21 T |
| 22 S | 22 W | 22 F |
| 23 M | 23 T | 23 S |
| 24 T | 24 F | 24 S |
| 25 W | 25 S | 25 M |
| 26 T | 26 S | 26 T |
| 27 F | 27 M | 27 W |
| 28 S | 28 T | 28 T |
| 29 S | 29 W | 29 F |
| 30 M | 30 T | 30 S |
| 31 T | | 31 S |

JANUARY

### The Pink Orchard

**Vincent van Gogh (1853 - 1890),
Arles, beginning of April 1888**

When Van Gogh arrived in Arles (FR)
in February 1888, winter still held the
village in its grip. After a few weeks,
spring came. Full of enthusiasm, he
began a series of studies of trees in
blossom. When he saw the paintings
side by side, he had the idea of
combining them into triptychs. In a
triptych, three works are combined
into one harmonious whole. Van Gogh
was familiar with this idea from
Japanese prints.

Van Gogh went on to produce no fewer
than fourteen paintings of fruit trees
in blossom in the space of a month.
He hoped his orchard paintings would
sell. To his brother Theo he wrote, 'You
know these subjects are among the
ones that cheer everyone up.'

Van
Gogh
Museum
Amsterdam

## 26 MONDAY

## 27 TUESDAY

## 28 WEDNESDAY

## 29 THURSDAY

FRIDAY **30**

J

New Year's Eve    SATURDAY **31**

New Year's Day    SUNDAY **1**

'The lark can't be silent as long as it can sing.'

**Vincent van Gogh to his brother Theo, 18 November 1881**

Van Gogh Museum
Amsterdam

| T | F | S | S | M | T | W | T | F | S | S | M | T | W | T | F | S | S | M | T | W | T | F | S | S | M | T | W | T | F | S |
|---|---|---|---|---|---|---|---|---|---|---|---|---|---|---|---|---|---|---|---|---|---|---|---|---|---|---|---|---|---|---|
| 15 | 16 | 17 | 18 | 19 | 20 | 21 | 22 | 23 | 24 | 25 | 26 | 27 | 28 | 29 | 30 | 31 | 1 | 2 | 3 | 4 | 5 | 6 | 7 | 8 | 9 | 10 | 11 | 12 | 13 | 14 |

## 2 MONDAY

New Year Holiday

## 3 TUESDAY

Bank Holiday (Scotland)

## 4 WEDNESDAY

## 5 THURSDAY

FRIDAY **6**

J

---

SATURDAY **7**

---

SUNDAY **8**

---

**NOTES**

Van
Gogh
Museum

Amsterdam

| S | M | T | W | T | F | S | S | M | T | W | T | F | S | S | M | T | W | T | F | S | S | M | T | W | T | F | S | S | M | T |
|---|---|---|---|---|---|---|---|---|---|---|---|---|---|---|---|---|---|---|---|---|---|---|---|---|---|---|---|---|---|---|
| 1 | 2 | 3 | 4 | 5 | 6 | 7 | 8 | 9 | 10 | 11 | 12 | 13 | 14 | 15 | 16 | 17 | 18 | 19 | 20 | 21 | 22 | 23 | 24 | 25 | 26 | 27 | 28 | 29 | 30 | 31 |

## 9 MONDAY

## 10 TUESDAY

## 11 WEDNESDAY

## 12 THURSDAY

FRIDAY **13**

J

SATURDAY **14**

SUNDAY **15**

**NOTES**

Van
Gogh
Museum

Amsterdam

| S | M | T | W | T | F | S | S | M | T | W | T | F | S | S | M | T | W | T | F | S | S | M | T | W | T | F | S | S | M | T |
|---|---|---|---|---|---|---|---|---|---|---|---|---|---|---|---|---|---|---|---|---|---|---|---|---|---|---|---|---|---|---|
| 1 | 2 | 3 | 4 | 5 | 6 | 7 | 8 | 9 | 10 | 11 | 12 | 13 | 14 | 15 | 16 | 17 | 18 | 19 | 20 | 21 | 22 | 23 | 24 | 25 | 26 | 27 | 28 | 29 | 30 | 31 |

## 16 MONDAY

## 17 TUESDAY

## 18 WEDNESDAY

## 19 THURSDAY

FRIDAY **20**

J

SATURDAY **21**

Chinese New Year (Rabbit)                                          SUNDAY **22**

## NOTES

Van
Gogh
Museum

Amsterdam

| S | M | T | W | T | F | S | S | M | T | W | T | F | S | S | M | T | W | T | F | S | S | M | T | W | T | F | S | S | M | T |
|---|---|---|---|---|---|---|---|---|---|---|---|---|---|---|---|---|---|---|---|---|---|---|---|---|---|---|---|---|---|---|
| 1 | 2 | 3 | 4 | 5 | 6 | 7 | 8 | 9 | 10 | 11 | 12 | 13 | 14 | 15 | 16 | 17 | 18 | 19 | 20 | 21 | 22 | 23 | 24 | 25 | 26 | 27 | 28 | 29 | 30 | 31 |

**23** MONDAY

**24** TUESDAY

**25** WEDNESDAY

**26** THURSDAY

FRIDAY **27**

J

SATURDAY **28**

SUNDAY **29**

## NOTES

Van
Gogh
Museum

Amsterdam

| S | M | T | W | T | F | S | S | M | T | W | T | F | S | S | M | T | W | T | F | S | S | M | T | W | T | F | S | S | M | T |
|---|---|---|---|---|---|---|---|---|---|---|---|---|---|---|---|---|---|---|---|---|---|---|---|---|---|---|---|---|---|---|
| 1 | 2 | 3 | 4 | 5 | 6 | 7 | 8 | 9 | 10 | 11 | 12 | 13 | 14 | 15 | 16 | 17 | 18 | 19 | 20 | 21 | 22 | 23 | 24 | 25 | 26 | 27 | 28 | 29 | 30 | 31 |

FEBRUARY

### The Yellow House (The Street)

**Vincent van Gogh (1853 - 1890),
Arles, September 1888**

In May 1888, Van Gogh rented four rooms in a house on Place Lamartine in Arles (southern France). The green shutters in this painting of the square show where he lived. Shortly after moving into the 'Yellow House', he sent Theo a description and sketch of his painting of it: 'it's tremendous, these yellow houses in the sunlight and then the incomparable freshness of the blue.'

The work, which Van Gogh himself called 'The Street', records the artist's immediate surroundings: he often ate at the restaurant on the left, and the home of his friend, the postman Joseph Roulin, lay just beyond the second railway bridge.

Vincent had finally found a place at the Yellow House where he could not only paint but also have his friends come to stay. His plan was to turn the yellow corner-building into an artists' house, where like-minded painters could live and work together.

## 30 MONDAY

## 31 TUESDAY

## 1 WEDNESDAY

## 2 THURSDAY

FRIDAY **3**

F

SATURDAY **4**

SUNDAY **5**

'There's a lot more to love than people usually think.'

**Vincent van Gogh to his brother Theo, 31 July 1874**

Van
Gogh
Museum
Amsterdam

## 6  MONDAY

## 7  TUESDAY

## 8  WEDNESDAY

## 9  THURSDAY

FRIDAY **10**

SATURDAY **11**

SUNDAY **12**

## NOTES

Van
Gogh
Museum
Amsterdam

| W | T | F | S | S | M | T | W | T | F | S | S | M | T | W | T | F | S | S | M | T | W | T | F | S | S | M | T |
|---|---|---|---|---|---|---|---|---|---|---|---|---|---|---|---|---|---|---|---|---|---|---|---|---|---|---|---|
| 1 | 2 | 3 | 4 | 5 | 6 | 7 | 8 | 9 | 10 | 11 | 12 | 13 | 14 | 15 | 16 | 17 | 18 | 19 | 20 | 21 | 22 | 23 | 24 | 25 | 26 | 27 | 28 |

## 13 MONDAY

## 14 TUESDAY

Valentine's Day

## 15 WEDNESDAY

## 16 THURSDAY

FRIDAY **17**

F

SATURDAY **18**

SUNDAY **19**

**NOTES**

Van
Gogh
Museum
Amsterdam

| W | T | F | S | S | M | T | W | T | F | S | S | M | T | W | T | F | S | S | M | T | W | T | F | S | S | M | T |
|---|---|---|---|---|---|---|---|---|---|---|---|---|---|---|---|---|---|---|---|---|---|---|---|---|---|---|---|
| 1 | 2 | 3 | 4 | 5 | 6 | 7 | 8 | 9 | 10 | 11 | 12 | 13 | 14 | 15 | 16 | 17 | 18 | 19 | 20 | 21 | 22 | 23 | 24 | 25 | 26 | 27 | 28 |

## 20 MONDAY

## 21 TUESDAY

Shrove Tuesday

## 22 WEDNESDAY

## 23 THURSDAY

## FRIDAY 24

F

## SATURDAY 25

## SUNDAY 26

## NOTES

**Van Gogh Museum**
Amsterdam

| W | T | F | S | S | M | T | W | T | F | S | S | M | T | W | T | F | S | S | M | T | W | T | F | S | S | M | T |
|---|---|---|---|---|---|---|---|---|---|---|---|---|---|---|---|---|---|---|---|---|---|---|---|---|---|---|---|
| 1 | 2 | 3 | 4 | 5 | 6 | 7 | 8 | 9 | 10 | 11 | 12 | 13 | 14 | 15 | 16 | 17 | 18 | 19 | 20 | 21 | 22 | 23 | 24 | 25 | 26 | 27 | 28 |

MARCH

### *Red Cabbages and Onions*

**Vincent van Gogh (1853 - 1890),
Paris, October-November 1887**

Van Gogh could not have chosen a simpler
subject: some onions and a few red cabbages.
But by working with colour contrasts, he was
able to turn them into something special.

It's important to realise that the colours in
this still life have changed over time. The
tablecloth is now greyish-blue but was
originally purple. That formed a strong contrast
with the yellow of the onions and of the right
upper background.

Van
Gogh
Museum

Amsterdam

## 27 MONDAY

## 28 TUESDAY

## 1 WEDNESDAY

St. David's Day

## 2 THURSDAY

FRIDAY 3

SATURDAY 4

SUNDAY 5

'Do right and don't look back, and things will turn out well.'

Vincent van Gogh to his brother Theo, 30 April 1874

Van Gogh Museum
Amsterdam

| W | T | F | S | S | M | T | W | T | F | S | S | M | T | W | T | F | S | S | M | T | W | T | F | S | S | M | T |
|---|---|---|---|---|---|---|---|---|---|---|---|---|---|---|---|---|---|---|---|---|---|---|---|---|---|---|---|
| 15 | 16 | 17 | 18 | 19 | 20 | 21 | 22 | 23 | 24 | 25 | 26 | 27 | 28 | 1 | 2 | 3 | 4 | 5 | 6 | 7 | 8 | 9 | 10 | 11 | 12 | 13 | 14 |

## 6 MONDAY

## 7 TUESDAY

## 8 WEDNESDAY

## 9 THURSDAY

FRIDAY **10**

M

SATURDAY **11**

SUNDAY **12**

**NOTES**

Van
Gogh
Museum

Amsterdam

W T F S S M T W T F S S M T W T F S S M T W T F S S M T W T F
1 2 3 4 5 6 7 8 9 10 11 12 13 14 15 16 17 18 19 20 21 22 23 24 25 26 27 28 29 30 31

## 13 MONDAY

## 14 TUESDAY

## 15 WEDNESDAY

## 16 THURSDAY

St. Patrick's Day | FRIDAY **17**

M

SATURDAY **18**

Mothering Sunday (UK) | SUNDAY **19**

## NOTES

Van
Gogh
Museum
Amsterdam

| W | T | F | S | S | M | T | W | T | F | S | S | M | T | W | T | F | S | S | M | T | W | T | F | S | S | M | T | W | T | F |
|---|---|---|---|---|---|---|---|---|---|---|---|---|---|---|---|---|---|---|---|---|---|---|---|---|---|---|---|---|---|---|
| 1 | 2 | 3 | 4 | 5 | 6 | 7 | 8 | 9 | 10 | 11 | 12 | 13 | 14 | 15 | 16 | 17 | 18 | 19 | 20 | 21 | 22 | 23 | 24 | 25 | 26 | 27 | 28 | 29 | 30 | 31 |

## 20 MONDAY

## 21 TUESDAY

## 22 WEDNESDAY

Ramadan Begins

## 23 THURSDAY

FRIDAY **24**

M

SATURDAY **25**

Daylight Saving Time Starts

SUNDAY **26**

## NOTES

Van
Gogh
Museum

Amsterdam

| W | T | F | S | S | M | T | W | T | F | S | S | M | T | W | T | F | S | S | M | T | W | T | F | S | S | M | T | W | T | F |
|---|---|---|---|---|---|---|---|---|---|---|---|---|---|---|---|---|---|---|---|---|---|---|---|---|---|---|---|---|---|---|
| 1 | 2 | 3 | 4 | 5 | 6 | 7 | 8 | 9 | 10 | 11 | 12 | 13 | 14 | 15 | 16 | 17 | 18 | 19 | 20 | 21 | 22 | 23 | 24 | 25 | 26 | 27 | 28 | 29 | 30 | 31 |

*Allotment with Sunflower*

**Vincent van Gogh (1853 - 1890),
Paris, July 1887**

The huge sunflower is clearly the main subject
of this painting. Van Gogh was very fond of this
flower. In southern France, he painted large
bouquets of sunflowers. And during his earlier
Paris period, he devoted a series of still lifes to
this subject.

Van Gogh made this painting on the hill of
Montmartre in Paris. In the background, a
little bit of the city is visible. On the left are the
chimneys of the factories in the Clichy district. He
painted this city scene on the back of the painting
Head of a Woman, which he had made earlier in
Nuenen (NL). This was a way of saving expensive
linen canvas.

Van
Gogh
Museum
Amsterdam

**27** MONDAY

**28** TUESDAY

**29** WEDNESDAY

**30** THURSDAY

FRIDAY **31**

SATURDAY **1**

**A**

SUNDAY **2**

'I'd rather fail than sit idle.'

**Vincent van Gogh to his brother Theo, 14 July 1885**

Van
Gogh
Museum
Amsterdam

| T | F | S | S | M | T | W | T | F | S | S | M | T | W | T | F | S | S | M | T | W | T | F | S | S | M | T | W | T | F | S |
|---|---|---|---|---|---|---|---|---|---|---|---|---|---|---|---|---|---|---|---|---|---|---|---|---|---|---|---|---|---|---|
| 16 | 17 | 18 | 19 | 20 | 21 | 22 | 23 | 24 | 25 | 26 | 27 | 28 | 29 | 30 | 31 | 1 | 2 | 3 | 4 | 5 | 6 | 7 | 8 | 9 | 10 | 11 | 12 | 13 | 14 | 15 |

## 3 MONDAY

## 4 TUESDAY

## 5 WEDNESDAY

Passover Begins

## 6 THURSDAY

Good Friday                                                             FRIDAY **7**

**A**

SATURDAY **8**

Easter Sunday                                          SUNDAY **9**

## NOTES

Van
Gogh
Museum
Amsterdam

| S | S | M | T | W | T | F | S | S | M | T | W | T | F | S | S | M | T | W | T | F | S | S | M | T | W | T | F | S | S |
|---|---|---|---|---|---|---|---|---|---|---|---|---|---|---|---|---|---|---|---|---|---|---|---|---|---|---|---|---|---|
| 1 | 2 | 3 | 4 | 5 | 6 | 7 | 8 | 9 | 10 | 11 | 12 | 13 | 14 | 15 | 16 | 17 | 18 | 19 | 20 | 21 | 22 | 23 | 24 | 25 | 26 | 27 | 28 | 29 | 30 |

## 10 MONDAY

Easter Monday

## 11 TUESDAY

## 12 WEDNESDAY

## 13 THURSDAY

FRIDAY **14**

SATURDAY **15**

A

SUNDAY **16**

**NOTES**

Van
Gogh
Museum

Amsterdam

| S | S | M | T | W | T | F | S | S | M | T | W | T | F | S | S | M | T | W | T | F | S | S | M | T | W | T | F | S | S |
|---|---|---|---|---|---|---|---|---|---|---|---|---|---|---|---|---|---|---|---|---|---|---|---|---|---|---|---|---|---|
| 1 | 2 | 3 | 4 | 5 | 6 | 7 | 8 | 9 | 10 | 11 | 12 | 13 | 14 | 15 | 16 | 17 | 18 | 19 | 20 | 21 | 22 | 23 | 24 | 25 | 26 | 27 | 28 | 29 | 30 |

## 17 MONDAY

## 18 TUESDAY

## 19 WEDNESDAY

## 20 THURSDAY

## FRIDAY 21

A

Earth Day                                                SATURDAY 22

St. George's Day                                          SUNDAY 23

## NOTES

Van
Gogh
Museum
Amsterdam

| S | S | M | T | W | T | F | S | S | M | T | W | T | F | S | S | M | T | W | T | F | S | S | M | T | W | T | F | S | S |
|---|---|---|---|---|---|---|---|---|---|---|---|---|---|---|---|---|---|---|---|---|---|---|---|---|---|---|---|---|---|
| 1 | 2 | 3 | 4 | 5 | 6 | 7 | 8 | 9 | 10 | 11 | 12 | 13 | 14 | 15 | 16 | 17 | 18 | 19 | 20 | 21 | 22 | 23 | 24 | 25 | 26 | 27 | 28 | 29 | 30 |

## 24 MONDAY

## 25 TUESDAY

## 26 WEDNESDAY

## 27 THURSDAY

FRIDAY **28**

SATURDAY **29**

M

SUNDAY **30**

## NOTES

Van
Gogh
Museum

Amsterdam

S S M T W T F S S M T W T F S S M T W T F S S M T W T F S S
1 2 3 4 5 6 7 8 9 10 11 12 13 14 15 16 17 18 19 20 21 22 23 24 25 26 27 28 29 30

MAY

### *Field with Irises near Arles*

**Vincent van Gogh (1853 - 1890),**
**Arles, May 1888**

Van Gogh was captivated by the colours of the landscape around the town of Arles (FR). He particularly loved the contrast between the yellow and purple flowers in the fields.

In the landscape, he felt he could see a reflection of the world he knew from his collection of Japanese prints. Japanese artists used large areas of colour in their compositions, often with a sharp diagonal. They also regularly zoomed in on a detail in the foreground. Van Gogh adopted these elements in his paintings. It was just like 'a Japanese dream,' he wrote in a letter to his brother Theo.

The painting was recently examined and restored. In the process, the old discoloured varnish layer which had dulled the colours was removed. The colours are now much brighter.

**1** MONDAY
Early May Bank Holiday

**2** TUESDAY

**3** WEDNESDAY

**4** THURSDAY

FRIDAY **5**

SATURDAY **6**

M

SUNDAY **7**

'The conscience is a
man's compass'

Vincent van Gogh to his brother Theo, 18 December 1882

Van
Gogh
Museum
Amsterdam

M T W T F S S M T W T F S S M T W T F S S M T W T F S S M T W
1 2 3 4 5 6 7 8 9 10 11 12 13 14 15 16 17 18 19 20 21 22 23 24 25 26 27 28 29 30 31

**8** MONDAY

**9** TUESDAY

**10** WEDNESDAY

**11** THURSDAY

FRIDAY **12**

SATURDAY **13**

M

SUNDAY **14**

**NOTES**

Van
Gogh
Museum

Amsterdam

M T W T F S S M T W T F S S M T W T F S S M T W T F S S M T W
1 2 3 4 5 6 7 8 9 10 11 12 13 14 15 16 17 18 19 20 21 22 23 24 25 26 27 28 29 30 31

**15** MONDAY

**16** TUESDAY

**17** WEDNESDAY

**18** THURSDAY

FRIDAY **19**

SATURDAY **20**

M

SUNDAY **21**

**NOTES**

Van
Gogh
Museum
Amsterdam

| M | T | W | T | F | S | S | M | T | W | T | F | S | S | M | T | W | T | F | S | S | M | T | W | T | F | S | S | M | T | W |
|---|---|---|---|---|---|---|---|---|---|---|---|---|---|---|---|---|---|---|---|---|---|---|---|---|---|---|---|---|---|---|
| 1 | 2 | 3 | 4 | 5 | 6 | 7 | 8 | 9 | 10 | 11 | 12 | 13 | 14 | 15 | 16 | 17 | 18 | 19 | 20 | 21 | 22 | 23 | 24 | 25 | 26 | 27 | 28 | 29 | 30 | 31 |

## 22 MONDAY

## 23 TUESDAY

## 24 WEDNESDAY

## 25 THURSDAY

## FRIDAY 26

## SATURDAY 27

M

## SUNDAY 28

**NOTES**

Van
Gogh
Museum

Amsterdam

JUNE

## Boulevard de Clichy

**Vincent van Gogh (1853 - 1890),
Paris, March-April 1887**

Boulevard de Clichy is one of the
major streets in the Paris district of
Montmartre, where many artists lived.
Van Gogh painted the junction that he
often crossed. Rue Lepic, where he lived
with his brother Theo, began on the right,
just beyond the edge of the picture.

In Paris, Van Gogh was exposed to
the latest art movements of his day,
Impressionism and Pointillism. This
gradually led him to use lighter colours.
He also experimented with a variety
of painting techniques. His style of
brushwork, with many dashes of paint
side by side, shows the influence of these
art movements. In the same paintings, he
also tried out diluted oil paint.

**29** MONDAY                                                    Spring Bank Holiday

**30** TUESDAY

**31** WEDNESDAY

**1** THURSDAY

FRIDAY **2**

SATURDAY **3**

J

SUNDAY **4**

'Find things beautiful as much
as you can. Most people find
too little beautiful.'

**Vincent van Gogh to his brother Theo, January 1874**

Van
Gogh
Museum
Amsterdam

T W T F S S M T W T F S S M T W T F S S M T W T F S S M T W T
16 17 18 19 20 21 22 23 24 25 26 27 28 29 30 31 | 1 2 3 4 5 6 7 8 9 10 11 12 13 14 15

## 5 MONDAY

## 6 TUESDAY

## 7 WEDNESDAY

## 8 THURSDAY

FRIDAY **9**

SATURDAY **10**

J

SUNDAY **11**

**NOTES**

Van
Gogh
Museum

Amsterdam

| T | F | S | S | M | T | W | T | F | S | S | M | T | W | T | F | S | S | M | T | W | T | F | S | S | M | T | W | T | F |
|---|---|---|---|---|---|---|---|---|---|---|---|---|---|---|---|---|---|---|---|---|---|---|---|---|---|---|---|---|---|
| 1 | 2 | 3 | 4 | 5 | 6 | 7 | 8 | 9 | 10 | 11 | 12 | 13 | 14 | 15 | 16 | 17 | 18 | 19 | 20 | 21 | 22 | 23 | 24 | 25 | 26 | 27 | 28 | 29 | 30 |

## 12 MONDAY

## 13 TUESDAY

## 14 WEDNESDAY

## 15 THURSDAY

FRIDAY **16**

SATURDAY **17**

J

Father's Day (UK)                                    SUNDAY **18**

## NOTES

Van
Gogh
Museum

Amsterdam

| T | F | S | S | M | T | W | T | F | S | S | M | T | W | T | F | S | S | M | T | W | T | F | S | S | M | T | W | T | F |
|---|---|---|---|---|---|---|---|---|---|---|---|---|---|---|---|---|---|---|---|---|---|---|---|---|---|---|---|---|---|
| 1 | 2 | 3 | 4 | 5 | 6 | 7 | 8 | 9 | 10 | 11 | 12 | 13 | 14 | 15 | 16 | 17 | 18 | 19 | 20 | 21 | 22 | 23 | 24 | 25 | 26 | 27 | 28 | 29 | 30 |

## 19 MONDAY

## 20 TUESDAY

## 21 WEDNESDAY

## 22 THURSDAY

FRIDAY **23**

SATURDAY **24**

J

SUNDAY **25**

**NOTES**

Van
Gogh
Museum

Amsterdam

| T | F | S | S | M | T | W | T | F | S | S | M | T | W | T | F | S | S | M | T | W | T | F | S | S | M | T | W | T | F |
|---|---|---|---|---|---|---|---|---|---|---|---|---|---|---|---|---|---|---|---|---|---|---|---|---|---|---|---|---|---|
| 1 | 2 | 3 | 4 | 5 | 6 | 7 | 8 | 9 | 10 | 11 | 12 | 13 | 14 | 15 | 16 | 17 | 18 | 19 | 20 | 21 | 22 | 23 | 24 | 25 | 26 | 27 | 28 | 29 | 30 |

*Self-Portrait*

**Vincent van Gogh (1853 - 1890),**
**Paris, March-June 1887**

Around the world, people recognise this man
with a red beard and an earnest look in his eyes.
Vincent van Gogh painted about 35 self-portraits
in total, most of them in Paris. For him, this was a
way of practising portrait painting. His intention
was not to portray himself as realistically as
possible. He used the Neo-Impressionist style
here, with short, rough brushstrokes. These
alternate with longer strokes, such as the orange
in his beard.

The background was originally purple (a mix of
red and blue), but the red pigment has discoloured
and has become almost completely transparent.

## 26 MONDAY

## 27 TUESDAY

## 28 WEDNESDAY

## 29 THURSDAY

FRIDAY **30**

SATURDAY **1**

SUNDAY **2**

J

'Let's paint a lot and be productive and be ourselves with faults and qualities.'

**Vincent van Gogh to his brother Theo, 9 April 1885**

Van
Gogh
Museum
Amsterdam

| F | S | S | M | T | W | T | F | S | S | M | T | W | T | F | S | S | M | T | W | T | F | S | S | M | T | W | T | F | S |
|---|---|---|---|---|---|---|---|---|---|---|---|---|---|---|---|---|---|---|---|---|---|---|---|---|---|---|---|---|---|
| 16 | 17 | 18 | 19 | 20 | 21 | 22 | 23 | 24 | 25 | 26 | 27 | 28 | 29 | 30 | 1 | 2 | 3 | 4 | 5 | 6 | 7 | 8 | 9 | 10 | 11 | 12 | 13 | 14 | 15 |

## 3   MONDAY

## 4   TUESDAY

## 5   WEDNESDAY

## 6   THURSDAY

FRIDAY **7**

SATURDAY **8**

J

SUNDAY **9**

**NOTES**

Van
Gogh
Museum
Amsterdam

S S M T W T F S S M T W T F S S M T W T F S S M T W T F S S M
1 2 3 4 5 6 7 8 9 10 11 12 13 14 15 16 17 18 19 20 21 22 23 24 25 26 27 28 29 30 31

## 10 MONDAY

## 11 TUESDAY

## 12 WEDNESDAY      Public Holiday (Northern Ireland)

## 13 THURSDAY

FRIDAY **14**

SATURDAY **15**

J

SUNDAY **16**

**NOTES**

Van
Gogh
Museum
Amsterdam

| S | S | M | T | W | T | F | S | S | M | T | W | T | F | S | S | M | T | W | T | F | S | S | M | T | W | T | F | S | S | M |
|---|---|---|---|---|---|---|---|---|---|---|---|---|---|---|---|---|---|---|---|---|---|---|---|---|---|---|---|---|---|---|
| 1 | 2 | 3 | 4 | 5 | 6 | 7 | 8 | 9 | 10 | 11 | 12 | 13 | 14 | 15 | 16 | 17 | 18 | 19 | 20 | 21 | 22 | 23 | 24 | 25 | 26 | 27 | 28 | 29 | 30 | 31 |

## 17 MONDAY

## 18 TUESDAY

Islamic New Year Begins

## 19 WEDNESDAY

## 20 THURSDAY

FRIDAY **21**

SATURDAY **22**

J

SUNDAY **23**

**NOTES**

Van
Gogh
Museum

Amsterdam

S S M T W T F S S M T W T F S S M T W T F S S M T W T F S S M
1  2  3  4  5  6  7  8  9 10 11 12 13 14 15 16 17 18 19 20 21 22 23 24 25 26 27 28 29 30 31

## 24 MONDAY

## 25 TUESDAY

## 26 WEDNESDAY

## 27 THURSDAY

### FRIDAY 28

### SATURDAY 29

### SUNDAY 30

## NOTES

Van
Gogh
Museum
Amsterdam

| S | S | M | T | W | T | F | S | S | M | T | W | T | F | S | S | M | T | W | T | F | S | S | M | T | W | T | F | S | S | M |
|---|---|---|---|---|---|---|---|---|---|---|---|---|---|---|---|---|---|---|---|---|---|---|---|---|---|---|---|---|---|---|
| 1 | 2 | 3 | 4 | 5 | 6 | 7 | 8 | 9 | 10 | 11 | 12 | 13 | 14 | 15 | 16 | 17 | 18 | 19 | 20 | 21 | 22 | 23 | 24 | 25 | 26 | 27 | 28 | 29 | 30 | 31 |

AUGUST

## *Wheatfield with a Reaper*

**Vincent van Gogh (1853 - 1890),
Saint-Rémy-de-Provence, September 1889**

Van Gogh painted this walled field from his hospital room. For the first few months that he was there, he was not allowed to leave the grounds.

The reaper labours in the heat of the sun. The wheat, painted with thick gobs of yellow, undulates around him. For Van Gogh, wheat was a symbol of the eternal cycle of nature and the transience of life. He saw the reaper as 'the image of death... in this sense that humanity would be the wheat being reaped.'

He added, however, that this death was 'almost smiling. It's all yellow except for a line of violet hills – a pale, blond yellow. I myself find that funny, that I saw it like that through the iron bars of a cell.'

Van
Gogh
Museum
Amsterdam

## 31 MONDAY

## 1 TUESDAY

## 2 WEDNESDAY

## 3 THURSDAY

FRIDAY **4**

SATURDAY **5**

SUNDAY **6**

A

'I have nature and art and poetry, and if that isn't enough, what is?'

**Vincent van Gogh to his brother Theo, January 1874**

| S | M | T | W | T | F | S | S | M | T | W | T | F | S | S | M | T | W | T | F | S | S | M | T | W | T | F | S | S | M | T |
|---|---|---|---|---|---|---|---|---|---|---|---|---|---|---|---|---|---|---|---|---|---|---|---|---|---|---|---|---|---|---|
| 16 | 17 | 18 | 19 | 20 | 21 | 22 | 23 | 24 | 25 | 26 | 27 | 28 | 29 | 30 | 31 | 1 | 2 | 3 | 4 | 5 | 6 | 7 | 8 | 9 | 10 | 11 | 12 | 13 | 14 | 15 |

## 7 MONDAY

Summer Bank Holiday (Scotland)

## 8 TUESDAY

## 9 WEDNESDAY

## 10 THURSDAY

FRIDAY **11**

SATURDAY **12**

SUNDAY **13**

**A**

**NOTES**

Van
Gogh
Museum

Amsterdam

| T | W | T | F | S | S | M | T | W | T | F | S | S | M | T | W | T | F | S | S | M | T | W | T | F | S | S | M | T | W | T |
|---|---|---|---|---|---|---|---|---|---|---|---|---|---|---|---|---|---|---|---|---|---|---|---|---|---|---|---|---|---|---|
| 1 | 2 | 3 | 4 | 5 | 6 | 7 | 8 | 9 | 10 | 11 | 12 | 13 | 14 | 15 | 16 | 17 | 18 | 19 | 20 | 21 | 22 | 23 | 24 | 25 | 26 | 27 | 28 | 29 | 30 | 31 |

## 14 MONDAY

## 15 TUESDAY

## 16 WEDNESDAY

## 17 THURSDAY

FRIDAY **18**

SATURDAY **19**

SUNDAY **20**

A

## NOTES

Van
Gogh
Museum

Amsterdam

| T | W | T | F | S | S | M | T | W | T | F | S | S | M | T | W | T | F | S | S | M | T | W | T | F | S | S | M | T | W | T |
|---|---|---|---|---|---|---|---|---|---|---|---|---|---|---|---|---|---|---|---|---|---|---|---|---|---|---|---|---|---|---|
| 1 | 2 | 3 | 4 | 5 | 6 | 7 | 8 | 9 | 10 | 11 | 12 | 13 | 14 | 15 | 16 | 17 | 18 | 19 | 20 | 21 | 22 | 23 | 24 | 25 | 26 | 27 | 28 | 29 | 30 | 31 |

## 21 MONDAY

## 22 TUESDAY

## 23 WEDNESDAY

## 24 THURSDAY

FRIDAY **25**

SATURDAY **26**

SUNDAY **27**

**A**

**NOTES**

Van
Gogh
Museum

Amsterdam

| T | W | T | F | S | S | M | T | W | T | F | S | S | M | T | W | T | F | S | S | M | T | W | T | F | S | S | M | T | W | T |
|---|---|---|---|---|---|---|---|---|---|---|---|---|---|---|---|---|---|---|---|---|---|---|---|---|---|---|---|---|---|---|
| 1 | 2 | 3 | 4 | 5 | 6 | 7 | 8 | 9 | 10 | 11 | 12 | 13 | 14 | 15 | 16 | 17 | 18 | 19 | 20 | 21 | 22 | 23 | 24 | 25 | 26 | 27 | 28 | 29 | 30 | 31 |

### Carafe and Dish with Citrus Fruit

**Vincent van Gogh (1853 - 1890),
Paris, February-March 1887**

Painting a glass object is difficult. Van Gogh
made the challenge even greater, choosing an
elaborate carafe and decorative wallpaper. This
made it necessary for him to render the colourful
reflections in the glass.

The tabletop underneath the dish of lemons is
tilted upward. This is not a mistake, but a choice.
Van Gogh was trying out a perspective technique
he had learned from Japanese woodcuts. Their
strong diagonals fascinated him. Vincent signed
and dated this still life. He did that only when he
was satisfied with his work.

Van
Gogh
Museum

Amsterdam

## 28 MONDAY

Summer Bank Holiday (ENG, NIR, WAL)

## 29 TUESDAY

## 30 WEDNESDAY

## 31 THURSDAY

FRIDAY **1**

SATURDAY **2**

SUNDAY **3**

S

'I always think that what we need is sunshine and fine weather and blue air as the most dependable remedy.'

**Vincent van Gogh to his brother Theo, 29 September 1888**

Van
Gogh
Museum
Amsterdam

W T F S S M T W T F S S M T W T F S S M T W T F S S M T W T F
16 17 18 19 20 21 22 23 24 25 26 27 28 29 30 31 | 1 2 3 4 5 6 7 8 9 10 11 12 13 14 15

## 4 MONDAY

## 5 TUESDAY

## 6 WEDNESDAY

## 7 THURSDAY

FRIDAY **8**

SATURDAY **9**

SUNDAY **10**

**S**

## NOTES

Van
Gogh
Museum
Amsterdam

| F | S | S | M | T | W | T | F | S | S | M | T | W | T | F | S | S | M | T | W | T | F | S | S | M | T | W | T | F | S |
|---|---|---|---|---|---|---|---|---|---|---|---|---|---|---|---|---|---|---|---|---|---|---|---|---|---|---|---|---|---|
| 1 | 2 | 3 | 4 | 5 | 6 | 7 | 8 | 9 | 10 | 11 | 12 | 13 | 14 | 15 | 16 | 17 | 18 | 19 | 20 | 21 | 22 | 23 | 24 | 25 | 26 | 27 | 28 | 29 | 30 |

## 11 MONDAY

## 12 TUESDAY

## 13 WEDNESDAY

## 14 THURSDAY

Rosh Hashanah (Jewish New Year) Begins

FRIDAY **15**

SATURDAY **16**

SUNDAY **17**

S

## NOTES

Van
Gogh
Museum
Amsterdam

## 18 MONDAY

## 19 TUESDAY

## 20 WEDNESDAY

## 21 THURSDAY

International Day of Peace (United Nations)

### FRIDAY 22

### SATURDAY 23

Yom Kippur Begins

### SUNDAY 24

S

## NOTES

Van
Gogh
Museum
Amsterdam

| F | S | S | M | T | W | T | F | S | S | M | T | W | T | F | S | S | S | M | T | W | T | F | S | S | M | T | W | T | F | S |
|---|---|---|---|---|---|---|---|---|---|---|---|---|---|---|---|---|---|---|---|---|---|---|---|---|---|---|---|---|---|---|
| 1 | 2 | 3 | 4 | 5 | 6 | 7 | 8 | 9 | 10 | 11 | 12 | 13 | 14 | 15 | 16 | 17 | 18 | 19 | 20 | 21 | 22 | 23 | 24 | 25 | 26 | 27 | 28 | 29 | 30 |

OCTOBER

### *Seascape near Les Saintes-Maries-de-la-Mer*

**Vincent van Gogh (1853 - 1890),
Arles, June 1888**

We can tell that Van Gogh painted this view of the sea from the beach, as grains of sand have been found in the paint layers. It was done at the fishing village of Les Saintes-Maries-de-la-Mer, during a trip he took from Arles in the south of France.

In addition to the blue and white that he brushed onto the canvas with bold strokes, he used green and yellow for the waves.

He applied these colours with a palette knife, neatly capturing the effect of the light through the waves. Van Gogh was enthusiastic about the colours of the Mediterranean Sea. He wrote that it 'has a colour like mackerel, in other words, changing – you don't always know if it's green or purple – you don't always know if it's blue – because a second later, its changing reflection has taken on a pink or grey hue'. The bright red signature has been placed prominently in the foreground: it was intended as a 'red note in the green'.

## 25 MONDAY

## 26 TUESDAY

## 27 WEDNESDAY

## 28 THURSDAY

FRIDAY **29**

SATURDAY **30**

SUNDAY **1**

'We are not alive in order to be happy, but we must try to deserve happiness.'

**Vincent van Gogh to his brother Theo, 10 December 1882**

Van Gogh Museum
Amsterdam

| S | S | M | T | W | T | F | S | S | M | T | W | T | F | S | S | M | T | W | T | F | S | S | M | T | W | T | F | S | S |
|---|---|---|---|---|---|---|---|---|---|---|---|---|---|---|---|---|---|---|---|---|---|---|---|---|---|---|---|---|---|
| 16 | 17 | 18 | 19 | 20 | 21 | 22 | 23 | 24 | 25 | 26 | 27 | 28 | 29 | 30 | 1 | 2 | 3 | 4 | 5 | 6 | 7 | 8 | 9 | 10 | 11 | 12 | 13 | 14 | 15 |

0

**2**  MONDAY

**3**  TUESDAY

**4**  WEDNESDAY

**5**  THURSDAY

FRIDAY **6**

SATURDAY **7**

SUNDAY **8**

O

**NOTES**

Van
Gogh
Museum

Amsterdam

| S | M | T | W | T | F | S | S | M | T | W | T | F | S | S | M | T | W | T | F | S | S | M | T | W | T | F | S | S | M | T |
|---|---|---|---|---|---|---|---|---|---|---|---|---|---|---|---|---|---|---|---|---|---|---|---|---|---|---|---|---|---|---|
| 1 | 2 | 3 | 4 | 5 | 6 | 7 | 8 | 9 | 10 | 11 | 12 | 13 | 14 | 15 | 16 | 17 | 18 | 19 | 20 | 21 | 22 | 23 | 24 | 25 | 26 | 27 | 28 | 29 | 30 | 31 |

## 9 MONDAY

## 10 TUESDAY

World Mental Health Day

## 11 WEDNESDAY

## 12 THURSDAY

FRIDAY **13**

SATURDAY **14**

SUNDAY **15**

O

**NOTES**

Van
Gogh
Museum
Amsterdam

| S | M | T | W | T | F | S | S | M | T | W | T | F | S | S | M | T | W | T | F | S | S | M | T | W | T | F | S | S | M | T |
|---|---|---|---|---|---|---|---|---|---|---|---|---|---|---|---|---|---|---|---|---|---|---|---|---|---|---|---|---|---|---|
| 1 | 2 | 3 | 4 | 5 | 6 | 7 | 8 | 9 | 10 | 11 | 12 | 13 | 14 | 15 | 16 | 17 | 18 | 19 | 20 | 21 | 22 | 23 | 24 | 25 | 26 | 27 | 28 | 29 | 30 | 31 |

## 16 MONDAY

## 17 TUESDAY

## 18 WEDNESDAY

## 19 THURSDAY

FRIDAY **20**

SATURDAY **21**

SUNDAY **22**

**0**

## NOTES

Van
Gogh
Museum

Amsterdam

S M T W T F S S M T W T F S S M T W T F S S M T W T F S S M T
1 2 3 4 5 6 7 8 9 10 11 12 13 14 15 16 17 18 19 20 21 22 23 24 25 26 27 28 29 30 31

**23** MONDAY

**24** TUESDAY

**25** WEDNESDAY

**26** THURSDAY

FRIDAY **27**

SATURDAY **28**

Daylight Saving Time Ends

SUNDAY **29**

0

## NOTES

Van
Gogh
Museum
Amsterdam

| S | M | T | W | T | F | S | S | M | T | W | T | F | S | S | M | T | W | T | F | S | S | M | T | W | T | F | S | S | M | T |
|---|---|---|---|---|---|---|---|---|---|---|---|---|---|---|---|---|---|---|---|---|---|---|---|---|---|---|---|---|---|---|
| 1 | 2 | 3 | 4 | 5 | 6 | 7 | 8 | 9 | 10 | 11 | 12 | 13 | 14 | 15 | 16 | 17 | 18 | 19 | 20 | 21 | 22 | 23 | 24 | 25 | 26 | 27 | 28 | 29 | 30 | 31 |

NOVEMBER

### Prawns and Mussels

**Vincent van Gogh (1853 - 1890),
Paris, September-November 1886**

Van Gogh always managed to find new
subjects for his still lifes. Here he used
shellfish. After painting them, he probably
had them for supper that same day.

His friend and fellow painter Paul Gauguin
(1848-1903) saw this small painting. Years
later, he mentioned it when writing about
his memories of Van Gogh. Gauguin said that
Van Gogh had sold the painting to a dealer
for five francs and given away the money
immediately afterwards to a poor young
woman in the street.

## 30 MONDAY

## 31 TUESDAY

Halloween

## 1 WEDNESDAY

## 2 THURSDAY

FRIDAY **3**

SATURDAY **4**

Guy Fawkes Night                                    SUNDAY **5**

'The sight of the stars always
makes me dream.'

**Vincent van Gogh to his brother Theo, 10 July 1888**

## 6 MONDAY

## 7 TUESDAY

## 8 WEDNESDAY

## 9 THURSDAY

## FRIDAY 10

## SATURDAY 11

Diwali / Remembrance Sunday                    SUNDAY 12

**N**

## NOTES

Van
Gogh
Museum
Amsterdam

| W | T | F | S | S | M | T | W | T | F | S | S | M | T | W | T | F | S | S | M | T | W | T | F | S | S | M | T | W | T |
|---|---|---|---|---|---|---|---|---|---|---|---|---|---|---|---|---|---|---|---|---|---|---|---|---|---|---|---|---|---|
| 1 | 2 | 3 | 4 | 5 | 6 | 7 | 8 | 9 | 10 | 11 | 12 | 13 | 14 | 15 | 16 | 17 | 18 | 19 | 20 | 21 | 22 | 23 | 24 | 25 | 26 | 27 | 28 | 29 | 30 |

## 13 MONDAY

## 14 TUESDAY

## 15 WEDNESDAY

## 16 THURSDAY

FRIDAY **17**

SATURDAY **18**

SUNDAY **19**

## NOTES

Van
Gogh
Museum
Amsterdam

| W | T | F | S | S | M | T | W | T | F | S | S | M | T | W | T | F | S | S | M | T | W | T | F | S | S | M | T | W | T |
|---|---|---|---|---|---|---|---|---|---|---|---|---|---|---|---|---|---|---|---|---|---|---|---|---|---|---|---|---|---|
| 1 | 2 | 3 | 4 | 5 | 6 | 7 | 8 | 9 | 10 | 11 | 12 | 13 | 14 | 15 | 16 | 17 | 18 | 19 | 20 | 21 | 22 | 23 | 24 | 25 | 26 | 27 | 28 | 29 | 30 |

## 20 MONDAY

## 21 TUESDAY

## 22 WEDNESDAY

## 23 THURSDAY

FRIDAY **24**

SATURDAY **25**

SUNDAY **26**

**NOTES**

Van
Gogh
Museum
Amsterdam

| W | T | F | S | S | M | T | W | T | F | S | S | M | T | W | T | F | S | S | M | T | W | T | F | S | S | M | T | W | T |
|---|---|---|---|---|---|---|---|---|---|---|---|---|---|---|---|---|---|---|---|---|---|---|---|---|---|---|---|---|---|
| 1 | 2 | 3 | 4 | 5 | 6 | 7 | 8 | 9 | 10 | 11 | 12 | 13 | 14 | 15 | 16 | 17 | 18 | 19 | 20 | 21 | 22 | 23 | 24 | 25 | 26 | 27 | 28 | 29 | 30 |

N

DECEMBER

### *Snow-Covered Field with a Harrow (after Millet)*

**Vincent van Gogh (1853 - 1890),
Saint-Rémy-de-Provence, January 1890**

After a long period of psychological crisis, Van Gogh had lost his confidence in himself, as a person and as a painter. For a long time, he felt useless and did not even dare to go outside. To build up his self-confidence again, he started copying prints – a common exercise for beginning painters.

This painting is a copy of a print by Jean-François Millet (1814-1875). Over the years, the colours have changed dramatically. The contrasts were originally much greater. It is now a bluish-green landscape, against which the black birds (crows or rooks) stand out strongly.

Van Gogh Museum

Amsterdam

## 27 MONDAY

## 28 TUESDAY

## 29 WEDNESDAY

## 30 THURSDAY

St. Andrew's Day

FRIDAY **1**

SATURDAY **2**

SUNDAY **3**

'If we made the colour very correct or the drawing very correct, we wouldn't create those emotions.'

**Vincent van Gogh to his brother Theo, 8 September 1888**

Van Gogh Museum Amsterdam

**D**

T F S S M T W T F S S M T W T | F S S M T W T F S S M T W T F
16 17 18 19 20 21 22 23 24 25 26 27 28 29 30 | 1 2 3 4 5 6 7 8 9 10 11 12 13 14 15

## 4 MONDAY

## 5 TUESDAY

## 6 WEDNESDAY

## 7 THURSDAY

FRIDAY **8**

SATURDAY **9**

SUNDAY **10**

**NOTES**

Van
Gogh
Museum

Amsterdam

D

| F | S | S | M | T | W | T | F | S | S | M | T | W | T | F | S | S | M | T | W | T | F | S | S | M | T | W | T | F | S | S |
|---|---|---|---|---|---|---|---|---|---|---|---|---|---|---|---|---|---|---|---|---|---|---|---|---|---|---|---|---|---|---|
| 1 | 2 | 3 | 4 | 5 | 6 | 7 | 8 | 9 | 10 | 11 | 12 | 13 | 14 | 15 | 16 | 17 | 18 | 19 | 20 | 21 | 22 | 23 | 24 | 25 | 26 | 27 | 28 | 29 | 30 | 31 |

## 11 MONDAY

## 12 TUESDAY

## 13 WEDNESDAY

## 14 THURSDAY

FRIDAY **15**

SATURDAY **16**

SUNDAY **17**

**NOTES**

Van
Gogh
Museum

Amsterdam

D

| F | S | S | M | T | W | T | F | S | S | M | T | W | T | F | S | S | M | T | W | T | F | S | S | M | T | W | T | F | S | S |
|---|---|---|---|---|---|---|---|---|---|---|---|---|---|---|---|---|---|---|---|---|---|---|---|---|---|---|---|---|---|---|
| 1 | 2 | 3 | 4 | 5 | 6 | 7 | 8 | 9 | 10 | 11 | 12 | 13 | 14 | 15 | 16 | 17 | 18 | 19 | 20 | 21 | 22 | 23 | 24 | 25 | 26 | 27 | 28 | 29 | 30 | 31 |

**18** MONDAY

**19** TUESDAY

**20** WEDNESDAY

**21** THURSDAY

### FRIDAY 22

### SATURDAY 23

### SUNDAY 24

**NOTES**

Van
Gogh
Museum
Amsterdam

D

| F | S | S | M | T | W | T | F | S | S | M | T | W | T | F | S | S | M | T | W | T | F | S | S | M | T | W | T | F | S | S |
|---|---|---|---|---|---|---|---|---|---|---|---|---|---|---|---|---|---|---|---|---|---|---|---|---|---|---|---|---|---|---|
| 1 | 2 | 3 | 4 | 5 | 6 | 7 | 8 | 9 | 10 | 11 | 12 | 13 | 14 | 15 | 16 | 17 | 18 | 19 | 20 | 21 | 22 | 23 | 24 | 25 | 26 | 27 | 28 | 29 | 30 | 31 |

## 25 MONDAY

Christmas Day

## 26 TUESDAY

Boxing Day

## 27 WEDNESDAY

## 28 THURSDAY

FRIDAY **29**

SATURDAY **30**

New Year's Eve                                    SUNDAY **31**

## NOTES

Van
Gogh
Museum
*Amsterdam*

D

F S S M T W T F S S M T W T F S S M T W T F S S M T W T F S S
1 2 3 4 5 6 7 8 9 10 11 12 13 14 15 16 17 18 19 20 21 22 23 24 25 26 27 28 29 30 31

# PLANNER 2024

| JANUARY | FEBRUARY | MARCH |
|---------|----------|-------|
| 1 M | 1 T | 1 F |
| 2 T | 2 F | 2 S |
| 3 W | 3 S | 3 S |
| 4 T | 4 S | 4 M |
| 5 F | 5 M | 5 T |
| 6 S | 6 T | 6 W |
| 7 S | 7 W | 7 T |
| 8 M | 8 T | 8 F |
| 9 T | 9 F | 9 S |
| 10 W | 10 S | 10 S |
| 11 T | 11 S | 11 M |
| 12 F | 12 M | 12 T |
| 13 S | 13 T | 13 W |
| 14 S | 14 W | 14 T |
| 15 M | 15 T | 15 F |
| 16 T | 16 F | 16 S |
| 17 W | 17 S | 17 S |
| 18 T | 18 S | 18 M |
| 19 F | 19 M | 19 T |
| 20 S | 20 T | 20 W |
| 21 S | 21 W | 21 T |
| 22 M | 22 T | 22 F |
| 23 T | 23 F | 23 S |
| 24 W | 24 S | 24 S |
| 25 T | 25 S | 25 M |
| 26 F | 26 M | 26 T |
| 27 S | 27 T | 27 W |
| 28 S | 28 W | 28 T |
| 29 M | 29 T | 29 F |
| 30 T | | 30 S |
| 31 W | | 31 S |

| APRIL | MAY | JUNE |
|---|---|---|
| 1 M | 1 W | 1 S |
| 2 T | 2 T | 2 S |
| 3 W | 3 F | 3 M |
| 4 T | 4 S | 4 T |
| 5 F | 5 S | 5 W |
| 6 S | 6 M | 6 T |
| 7 S | 7 T | 7 F |
| 8 M | 8 W | 8 S |
| 9 T | 9 T | 9 S |
| 10 W | 10 F | 10 M |
| 11 T | 11 S | 11 T |
| 12 F | 12 S | 12 W |
| 13 S | 13 M | 13 T |
| 14 S | 14 T | 14 F |
| 15 M | 15 W | 15 S |
| 16 T | 16 T | 16 S |
| 17 W | 17 F | 17 M |
| 18 T | 18 S | 18 T |
| 19 F | 19 S | 19 W |
| 20 S | 20 M | 20 T |
| 21 S | 21 T | 21 F |
| 22 M | 22 W | 22 S |
| 23 T | 23 T | 23 S |
| 24 W | 24 F | 24 M |
| 25 T | 25 S | 25 T |
| 26 F | 26 S | 26 W |
| 27 S | 27 M | 27 T |
| 28 S | 28 T | 28 F |
| 29 M | 29 W | 29 S |
| 30 T | 30 T | 30 S |
|  | 31 F |  |

# PLANNER 2024

| JULY | AUGUST | SEPTEMBER |
|------|--------|-----------|
| 1 M | 1 T | 1 S |
| 2 T | 2 F | 2 M |
| 3 W | 3 S | 3 T |
| 4 T | 4 S | 4 W |
| 5 F | 5 M | 5 T |
| 6 S | 6 T | 6 F |
| 7 S | 7 W | 7 S |
| 8 M | 8 T | 8 S |
| 9 T | 9 F | 9 M |
| 10 W | 10 S | 10 T |
| 11 T | 11 S | 11 W |
| 12 F | 12 M | 12 T |
| 13 S | 13 T | 13 F |
| 14 S | 14 W | 14 S |
| 15 M | 15 T | 15 S |
| 16 T | 16 F | 16 M |
| 17 W | 17 S | 17 T |
| 18 T | 18 S | 18 W |
| 19 F | 19 M | 19 T |
| 20 S | 20 T | 20 F |
| 21 S | 21 W | 21 S |
| 22 M | 22 T | 22 S |
| 23 T | 23 F | 23 M |
| 24 W | 24 S | 24 T |
| 25 T | 25 S | 25 W |
| 26 F | 26 M | 26 T |
| 27 S | 27 T | 27 F |
| 28 S | 28 W | 28 S |
| 29 M | 29 T | 29 S |
| 30 T | 30 F | 30 M |
| 31 W | 31 S | |

| OCTOBER | NOVEMBER | DECEMBER |
|---|---|---|
| 1 T | 1 F | 1 S |
| 2 W | 2 S | 2 M |
| 3 T | 3 S | 3 T |
| 4 F | 4 M | 4 W |
| 5 S | 5 T | 5 T |
| 6 S | 6 W | 6 F |
| 7 M | 7 T | 7 S |
| 8 T | 8 F | 8 S |
| 9 W | 9 S | 9 M |
| 10 T | 10 S | 10 T |
| 11 F | 11 M | 11 W |
| 12 S | 12 T | 12 T |
| 13 S | 13 W | 13 F |
| 14 M | 14 T | 14 S |
| 15 T | 15 F | 15 S |
| 16 W | 16 S | 16 M |
| 17 T | 17 S | 17 T |
| 18 F | 18 M | 18 W |
| 19 S | 19 T | 19 T |
| 20 S | 20 W | 20 F |
| 21 M | 21 T | 21 S |
| 22 T | 22 F | 22 S |
| 23 W | 23 S | 23 M |
| 24 T | 24 S | 24 T |
| 25 F | 25 M | 25 W |
| 26 S | 26 T | 26 T |
| 27 S | 27 W | 27 F |
| 28 M | 28 T | 28 S |
| 29 T | 29 F | 29 S |
| 30 W | 30 S | 30 M |
| 31 T | | 31 T |

# ADDRESS / PHONE NUMBERS

NAME:

ADDRESS:


TELEPHONE:                          MOBILE:

EMAIL:

NAME:

ADDRESS:


TELEPHONE:                          MOBILE:

EMAIL:

NAME:

ADDRESS:


TELEPHONE:                          MOBILE:

EMAIL:

NAME:

ADDRESS:


TELEPHONE:                          MOBILE:

EMAIL:

NAME:

ADDRESS:


TELEPHONE:                          MOBILE:

EMAIL:

NAME:

ADDRESS:


TELEPHONE:                          MOBILE:

EMAIL:

# ADDRESS / PHONE NUMBERS

NAME:

ADDRESS:


TELEPHONE: MOBILE:

EMAIL:

NAME:

ADDRESS:


TELEPHONE: MOBILE:

EMAIL:

NAME:

ADDRESS:


TELEPHONE: MOBILE:

EMAIL:

NAME:

ADDRESS:


TELEPHONE: MOBILE:

EMAIL:

NAME:

ADDRESS:


TELEPHONE: MOBILE:

EMAIL:

NAME:

ADDRESS:


TELEPHONE: MOBILE:

EMAIL:

'I feel that you create colours with
your words.'

**Vincent van Gogh to Albert Aurier, 9 February 1890**

# NOTES

'Be in no doubt, though - the way to succeed is to keep courage and patience, and to carry on working hard.'

**Vincent van Gogh to Albert Aurier, 9 February 1890**

v. gogh

**1**

Monsieur Th van Gogh

Maison Goupil et

13e Montmartre

Paris

heste to

wany it

adieu,

6

GOUPIL & Cie.

Éditeurs Imprimeurs

ESTAMPES FRANÇAISES & ÉTRANGÈRES

Tableaux Modernes

RUE CHAPTAL, 9, PARIS

Succursales à la Haye, Londres, Be

32

Paris,

Waarde Theo,

Een paar dagen geleden kr

van de Nittis, een gezicht

J'espère que celle-ci

t'arrive en bon état.

ne crains rien p

suis assez calme maintes

Laisse les faire. J'u se

peut-être bien d'écrire